6 Report

Dignity at the End of Life: What's Beneath the Assisted Dying Debate?

Andrew Grey

Foreword by Baroness Ilora
Finlay of Llandaff

Theos – enriching conversations

Theos exists to enrich the conversation about the role of faith in society.

Religion and faith have become key public issues in this century, nationally and globally. As our society grows more religiously diverse, we must grapple with religion as a significant force in public life. All too often, though, opinions in this area are reactionary or ill informed.

We exist to change this

We want to help people move beyond common misconceptions about faith and religion, behind the headlines and beneath the surface. Our rigorous approach gives us the ability to express informed views with confidence and clarity.

As the UK's leading religion and society think tank, we reach millions of people with our ideas. Through our reports, events and media commentary, we influence today's influencers and decision makers. According to *The Economist*, we're "an organisation that demands attention". We believe Christianity can contribute to the common good and that faith, given space in the public square, will help the UK to flourish.

Will you partner with us?

Theos receives no government, corporate or denominational funding. We rely on donations from individuals and organisations to continue our vital work. Please consider signing up as a Theos Friend or Associate or making a one off donation today.

Theos Friends and Students

— Stay up to date with our monthly newsletter

— Receive (free) printed copies of our reports

— Get free tickets to all our events

£75/ year
for Friends

£40/ year
for Students

Theos Associates

— Stay up to date with our monthly newsletter

— Receive (free) printed copies of our reports

— Get free tickets to all our events

— Get invites to private events with the Theos team and other Theos Associates

£375/ year

Sign up on our website:
www.theosthinktank.co.uk/about/support-us

Contents

Contents

Foreword

Cicely Saunders said that "dignity is having a sense of personal worth". How true. Over the years no other definition seems to have bettered this. But the components and behaviours that enhance a concept of personal worth, and therefore contribute to dignity, have been much discussed.

Respect for the person is a requirement of a civilised society, but making that happen at every level is challenging at best. Laws are more than just regulatory instruments. They also send social messages. An 'assisted dying' law sends the message, however unintended on the part of legislators, that if we are seriously ill taking our own lives is a course of action which it is appropriate to consider.

When it comes to dying, the inherent phobias of society emerge. In our post-modern world, the gap of access to care and resources has widened. Social care has to be paid for; funding often comes from the financial assets of the person needing care. Those dying with access to hospice care can experience what the Care Quality Commission has described as "an extremely high standard of care" and "a positive culture that is focused on providing person-centred care – treating people as people and not just as recipients of care".

When it comes to dying, some view assisted suicide and/or euthanasia as the solution to fears around death. Oregon's 1998 Death with Dignity Act implies by its very name that to have dignity at the end of life a person should opt for physician-assisted suicide. Indeed, the official data from Oregon over 19 years reveals that the reasons behind such suicides are mainly social rather than medical. Of those who died by taking lethal drugs supplied by a doctor, the main three reasons cited included being 'less able to engage in activities making life enjoyable', 'losing autonomy' and 'loss of dignity'.

Indeed, of late 'dignity' has been hijacked by advocates of 'assisted dying' and distorted to mean control over the means of one's death without regard to the much wider and more nuanced aspects of human dignity in all aspects of people's lives.

As this report acknowledges, dignity is not to be found simply in exercising personal control but through meaningful relationships with others. Such relationships recognise the intrinsic worth of every person, the interrelated nature of human behaviours and the fact that no one person is an island. This requires recognition that all domains – psychological, social, emotional, and spiritual – of a person's life contribute to and are essential components of their experience of a sense of dignity. It is also important to remember that our sense of our own dignity is often dependent on how we are treated by others: if we are treated harshly or dismissively, it is easy to feel that we – and our lives – are of little worth.

In recent years, Parliament – in both Westminster and Edinburgh – has considered at length whether it is possible to set realistic and robust conditions around assisted suicide that would provide effective safeguards to protect vulnerable people. While some have suggested that dignity would be enhanced by such legislation, others have pointed out that, while legalised 'assisted dying' might be seen by a minority of strong-willed people as enhancing their sense of dignity, it has the potential to put many more vulnerable people at risk of harm. Parliament, north and south of the border, has not been persuaded that a case for such legislation has been made.

With much discussion of how people die with dignity, the same conversation about how to help people live with dignity has been strikingly absent. That is the mission that we should focus on – and this report sets out some ways forward.

This report explores the theory and practice of the topic of dignity. It grapples with the ideological aspects of the concept and also builds on responses from professionals working on a daily basis with those nearing the end of life. It examines concepts of dignity in living, particularly in the face of deteriorating health, and develops a more informed view of what dignity really is, how it is respected and enhanced, and what it can and should look like for everyone.

Baroness Ilora Finlay of Llandaff

Introduction

In January 2014, the popular British television soap opera **Coronation Street** concluded a story about a well-loved character, Hayley Cropper, who had been living with pancreatic cancer. In the climactic episode, Hayley chose to die by drinking a concoction of toxic substances prepared by her husband Roy. The episode sparked a huge reaction on social media, with over 100,000 tweets.

These scenes were, of course, fictional. Yet Hayley's assisted death sparked a huge discussion, with a whole range of emotive messages sent in response to it. Art imitates life: cases of real people choosing and fighting for the legal right to an assisted death often gain comparable prominence in the media. Many members of the British public will be familiar with leading campaigners for assisted dying,[1] including Tony Nicklinson, who was paralysed from the neck down following a stroke in 2005 and described his life as a "living nightmare", before his death as a result of refusing food seven years later.[2] Equally well known is the case of Debbie Purdy, who had Multiple Sclerosis (MS) for almost twenty years and characterised her condition as "painful and uncomfortable," adding, "it's frightening and it's not how I want to live". She also died after refusing food, in 2013.[3]

More recently and in contrast to these cases, in 2015 national news media reported on the case of Gill Pharaoh, a palliative care nurse who was not living with any life-limiting conditions but chose to end her life at the Swiss clinic Dignitas as she did not want to experience the struggles she had seen older people face.

There have also been multiple features on assisted dying: ranging from films like the 2009 drama *A Short Stay in Switzerland,* inspired by the true story of a doctor with Motor

Neurone Disease (MND) travelling to Dignitas to end her own life, and the 2011 documentary *Choosing to Die*, in which Terry Pratchett, author of the famous Discworld novels, talked with a number of people who had life-limiting conditions, and whose loved one had such conditions, about their wishes regarding assisted dying. In June 2015, *The Economist* published a leading article expressing strong support for assisted dying.[4]

The public campaigning organisation Dignity in Dying claims that 82% of the British public supports a change in the law on assisted dying for the terminally ill.[5] Perhaps more surprisingly, research from 2013 suggested that 72% of Anglicans and 56% of Roman Catholics in the UK supported a change in the law.[6]

Political interest

The debate among British politicians on assisted dying and euthanasia is also long-standing, and testifies to the prominence of the issue in British societal discourse. In 1994, the House of Lords Select Committee on Medical Ethics considered voluntary euthanasia (the practice of administering lethal medication at the request of a person with a life-limiting condition) and concluded that there should be no change in the law to permit this practice, as it could be open to abuse.

A decade later, Lord Joel Joffe proposed the 'Assisted Dying for the Terminally Ill' Bill,[7] which was ultimately defeated. In 2014, a further ten years later, Lord Charles Falconer proposed a new 'Assisted Dying' Bill, which passed its initial readings in the House of Lords but ran out of time due to the Parliament ending in March 2015. In June 2015, Rob Marris, Labour MP for Wolverhampton South West, proposed a very similar Private Members' Bill to the House of Commons. On 11 September

2015, a significant majority of MPs voted against the Bill at its Second Reading.[8] The debate, however, is far from over.

The political interest in assisted dying is strongly connected to the public interest in the issue, with MPs receiving forceful and impassioned letters from constituents on both sides of the argument and taking them into account as they made their judgements on this complex issue. At the Second Reading debate, Rob Marris cited the aforementioned public opinion poll by Dignity in Dying as evidence that there was strong support for assisted dying.[9]

The wide interest of the British public in this topic is interesting: it suggests a broad recognition of the significance of the end of life, and a belief that certain values (whether rights, autonomy or compassion) need to be respected at this time. Yet at the same time, it is curious that the assisted dying debate seems to be the only aspect of end of life issues which gains such broad coverage in mainstream media, and which sparks such significant debate. When it comes to death and dying more generally, the topic is still a significant social taboo. Talking about it leaves most of us uncomfortable and is usually avoided where possible, and those who do refer to it are often accused of bringing a macabre or overly solemn tone to a conversation.

The taboo around death and dying

Most of us are reluctant to have conversations relating to death and dying even with our own loved ones, with the result that we often neglect to make important plans surrounding the care we want at the end of life, our funeral wishes, or ownership of our possessions.

Even healthcare professionals can neglect to have important conversations around death. According to the *National Care of the Dying Audit for Hospitals* 2014, over one in four bereaved relatives had not been told by hospital staff that their loved one was expected to die soon, and only 46% had been told what to expect when their loved one was dying.[10]

On one level, the taboo is unsurprising: reminding people of their mortality is unlikely to put them in the happiest of moods. Moreover, we do not have the same level of exposure to death as people had in the past. Just over a century ago, in 1901, average life expectancy in the UK was under 47 years.[11] Experiencing the deaths of relatives or friends was much more common. And of course, during the First and Second World Wars, with (for instance) 400,000 military deaths of British people during the latter, the experience was especially common.

Now in relative peacetime, with an average life expectancy in the UK of around 80 years, the experience of others dying is much less common. Whilst this is something to be grateful for, a side-effect is undoubtedly our reduced consciousness of death and dying – and a reluctance to be reminded of it in conversation.

So here we have juxtaposed two contrasting aspects of public conversation around the end of life: on the one hand, we talk very little about death and dying in themselves, yet on the other hand we talk at great length about one very specific issue – namely, whether people should be able to receive assistance from healthcare professionals to end their own lives.

The consequence of this tension is that many of us approach this issue without having necessarily considered the much broader aspect of our lives to which it is intrinsically related: the end of life. But it is not possible to grasp this issue properly without a broader framework for making sense of death and dying in themselves. If we extract assisted dying from this broader framework of dying, we isolate it from the context and thinking that give meaning to the rest of our lives. To redress this, this essay will explore questions relating to death and what matters at the end of life. In particular, it will focus on one of the most frequently used terms in debates on assisted dying – yet one that is rarely explained: dignity. This term is firmly embedded in the language of the debate – indeed, already in its first few pages this report has referred to the campaign organisation Dignity in Dying,[12] and the Swiss clinic Dignitas. There are numerous other examples, such as the Oregon state law permitting assisted dying, which is titled the Death with Dignity Act.

There is evidently a need to establish what is meant by such a prominently used term. This essay offers a perspective on dignity that draws on insights from Christian thought about the inalienable worth of every human being. This insight is based on an understanding of human beings as fundamentally "relational", a perspective that is informed by Christian theology but which is clearly comprehensible, and relevant, to anyone concerned with relationships and well-being, irrespective of their religious beliefs.[13]

The essay will explore the practical implications of this perspective on dignity, through interviews with professionals who have extensive experience of accompanying people at the end of life. This ensures that there is full reflection on dignity and death, resisting the tendency to consider assisted dying in isolation from these.

Relationality is at the heart of a Christian understanding of what it is to be human. This is based on the belief that all human beings are made in the image of a Trinitarian God whose nature is love and part of whose essence is to exist as three persons in relationship.

This theological voice is crucial for changing how the question of assisted dying is framed. Instead of starting from the point of whether we should grant a person's wish for assisted dying, Christian thought starts from the view of the person as relational, and therefore asks how best to respect the dignity that people at the end of life possess as persons in relationship.

The theological view is important but is often overlooked, perhaps because, as Chief Rabbi Ephraim Mirvis and Cardinal Vincent Nichols have argued, it is increasingly difficult to express religious views in popular public debates as they are dismissed as somehow less rational and worthy of a hearing than arguments that do not appeal to any overt religious principles.[14]

> Christian thought starts from the view of the person as relational, and therefore asks how best to respect the dignity that people at the end of life possess as persons in relationship.

This has certainly been evident in debates on assisted dying. When those arguing against assisted dying invoke faith – especially Christian faith – their arguments have sometimes been characterised as simplistic and based on the principle of the sanctity of life, which amount to 'no-one, religious or otherwise, should be able to take their own life, because God says so'. This characterisation is usually unfair and highly inaccurate, and is sometimes used to paraphrase arguments which did not even mention the phrase "sanctity of life".

It should also be noted that adherence to Christianity does not necessarily determine whether a person will support or oppose legalisation of assisted dying. It is well-known that the current Archbishop of Canterbury, the Most Revd Justin Welby, does not support a change in the law – but it came as a surprise to many when a former Archbishop of Canterbury, Dr George Carey, who is known for his background in the conservative evangelical wing of the Church of England, publicly expressed his support for assisted dying.[15] Where it is opposed by prominent clerics or lay Christians, the pattern is equally unpredictable – Dr Barry Morgan, the current Archbishop of Wales, who is known especially for his progressive views on other issues such as human sexuality, is opposed to legalising assisted dying.[16]

When religious leaders on either side of the debate argue their case, their appeals to theological concepts, far from simplifying the debate, add real depth to key ideas and terms that are commonly used in arguments on assisted dying but are not always justified or explained by those who use them. This applies not only to 'dignity', but also to terms such as love, compassion and rights, each of which has a much richer meaning in light of a broader framework of Christian language, images and ideas.

Exploring dignity

The first chapter of this essay explores the meaning of the term 'dignity' and its use in discussions of assisted dying, particularly in relation to an individual's choice and control over their life. Having argued that this understanding is inadequate, the next chapter will show that the term is better understood in light of the inalienable worth of human beings as relational, and places it within the context of the Christian story and creation in the image of God.

Having explored the meaning of dignity, the following chapter considers its implications for how to enable people to have a dignified death in practice: in particular, what it means to ensure that everyone has a 'good' *dignified* death, and what is required from clinicians, government, and the people who are important to those at the end of life, to make this possible. This discussion will be based on extensive insights from health and social care professionals with experience of caring for people at the end of life and supporting those who provide unpaid care for them. These insights come from a series of interviews with palliative care doctors, nurses and chaplains, about what the understanding of dignity set out in this essay looks like in practice for people at the end of life. These interviews offer an essential perspective, grounded in real experience, on the implications of this understanding of dignity for end of life care and assisted dying.

The essay will conclude that whilst support for assisted dying often arises (at least in part) from a desire to treat people with dignity at the end of life, this dignity is best honoured by investing the necessary time, money and resources into ensuring that every person has access to high quality end of life care, tailored to their specific needs and established through relationships between health and social care professionals and those at the end of life. As a result, every person who is approaching the end of life should be helped to feel valued as a human being, and as a member of their community and society as a whole. This will enable them to live, and to die, with dignity – in the fullest and truest sense of that word.

1 A note on terms: This essay uses the term 'assisted dying' to mean a person ending their own life with the assistance of a healthcare professional or any other person. This is primarily in the context of a person with a life-limiting condition terminating their life. Assisted dying is sometimes referred to as 'assisted suicide'. However, the latter term is sometimes taken to mean assisting someone who is not already approaching the end of life, to take their own life. To avoid this ambiguity, this essay uses the term 'assisted dying'. The essay is concerned specifically with assisted dying, rather than voluntary euthanasia, which is where someone else (often a healthcare professional) ends a person's life to relieve their suffering.

2 *BBC News*, 'Right-to-die man dead after refusing food', *www.bbc.co.uk/news/uk-england-19341722*, accessed 3 Dec 2015.

3 *The Guardian*, 'Assisted suicide campaigner Debbie Purdy dies aged 51', *www.theguardian.com/society/2014/dec/29/assisted-suicide-campaigner-debbie-purdy-dies*, accessed 3 Dec 2015.

4 *The Economist*, 'The right to die', *www.economist.com/news/leaders/21656182-doctors-should-be-allowed-help-suffering-and-terminally-ill-die-when-they-choose*, accessed 22 Nov 2015.

5 Dignity in Dying, *www.dignityindying.org.uk/*, accessed 22 Nov 2015.

6 Linda Woodhead, 'The Church of England: A Changing Church in a Changing Culture', *www.churchofengland.org/media/1793626/linda%20woodhead%20churchhouse-faithinresearch.ppt, accessed 22 Nov 2015.*

7 Hansard, House of Commons, *www.publications.parliament.uk/pa/ld200405/ldbills/004/2005004.pdf*, accessed 3 Dec 2015.

8 330 voted against the Bill, compared with 119 in favour, *www.publications.parliament.uk/pa/cm201516/cmhansrd/cm150911/debtext/150911-0002.htm*, accessed 23 July 2015.

9 Hansard, House of Commons, *www.publications.parliament.uk/pa/cm201516/cmhansrd/cm150911/debtext/150911-0001.htm*, accessed 3 Dec 2015.

10 Royal College of Physicians, 'National Care of the Dying Audit for Hospitals 2014', *www.rcplondon.ac.uk/projects/outputs/national-care-dying-audit-hospitals*, accessed 22 Nov 2015.

11 Max Roser (2015), 'Life Expectancy', Our WorldInData.org, *ourworldindata.org/data/population-growth-vital-statistics/life-expectancy/*, accessed 22 Nov 2015.

12 The use of 'Dignity' in this group's name is significant – formerly it was called the 'Voluntary Euthanasia Legalisation Society' (VELS). By changing the name it has helped to equate dignity with assisted dying.

13 This has been attested in numerous studies. See for example, JW Strawbridge et al, 'Religious attendance increases survival by improving and maintaining

good health behaviours, mental health, and social relationships', *Ann Behav Med.* 23(1) (2001) pp. 68-74.

[14] *The Telegraph*, 'Speaking about religion becoming an 'act of courage' in secular age – Chief Rabbi and Cardinal', *www.telegraph.co.uk/news/religion/11840439/ Speaking-about-religion-becoming-an-act-of-courage-in-secular-age-Chief-Rabbi-and-Cardinal.html*, accessed 3 Dec 2015.

[15] *BBC News*, 'Assisted dying: Ex-Archbishop of Canterbury Lord Carey backs bill', 12 July 2014, *www.bbc.co.uk/news/uk-28274531*, accessed 3 Dec 2015.

[16] *The Guardian*, 'Assisted dying: leaders of faith communities speak out against new bill', 5 Sep 2015, *www.theguardian.com/theobserver/2015/sep/05/assisted-dying-bill-leaders-faith-communities-letter-against*, accessed 3 Dec 2015.

1
Dignity in the assisted dying debate

The idea of dignity has, as the previous section demonstrated, long been central to the assisted dying debate, and the notion of dignity when people are dying is often associated with giving them this ability to end their own lives. This chapter will examine how dignity is used by proponents of assisted dying, before arguing that their understanding of dignity is usually inadequate.

Dignity and assisted dying

In 2015, a husband, father and businessman named Jeffrey Spector took the difficult decision to end his own life at Dignitas. He had inoperable cancer of the spine and was informed that any moment he could become paralysed from the waist down.

The prospect of this was unbearable for Jeffrey. He was quoted in the *Daily Mirror* explaining his rationale for going to Dignitas, citing his "human right to dignity". He elaborated on what that meant for him: "I want the ability to have a cup of tea and hold a phone. I want to be able to do those things myself."[1]

For Jeffrey, it was not just about the ability to have a cup of tea or phone conversation – but being able to manage those things by himself. Dignity was equated with independence. Part of retaining that independence was for him to take control over his death. Jeffrey explained that he "wanted control of the final stages of [his] life."[2]

Many of those who advocate assisted dying equate dignity with this choice to end one's own life. The Swiss organisation Dignitas, referred to in the introduction, has as its strapline, "to live with dignity – to die with dignity". Dignitas asserts that people "are the bearers of human dignity", and that "this is characterised most strongly when a person decides his or her own fate."[3] For Dignitas, making the choice to end one's own life is the ultimate expression of one's dignity as a human being.

Similarly, for Dignity in Dying, the group campaigning to legalise assisted dying, this goes to the heart of what it means to have a dignified death. The organisation lists three essential elements of this, two of which include in their wording, "*choice* over where we die" and "*control* over how we die" [emphases added].[4]

Parliamentarians who support assisted dying also use the language of dignity. During the debate on the Assisted Dying Bill on 11 September 2015, Conservative MP Crispin Blunt argued in favour of enabling people to "exercise the option of ending their life with dignity, at a time of their choosing". He urged his Conservative colleagues to support the Bill, as "the party of freedom and choice".[5]

What does dignity mean?

A helpful place to start when attempting to understand most words is to examine their etymologies. Of course, etymology cannot necessarily encapsulate every dimension of the meaning of a word, but it can point us in the right direction. The origins of 'dignity' are in the Latin word *dignitas*, from *dignus*, meaning 'worthy'.[6]

It is clear that for the organisations and individuals quoted above, dignity or worth at the end of life is about having the ability to make the individual choice as to when and how to end one's own life. Each of them emphasises strongly the elements of freedom, autonomy and choice.

Much of this emphasis draws, consciously or unconsciously, on the quintessentially modern idea of individualism. The primacy of the individual's choice is fundamental to this argument: sometimes even against the wishes of others in their life.

That recognised, the association of dignity with autonomy is not new. In particular, autonomy is intrinsic to philosopher Immanuel Kant's understanding of what it means to be human. It is crucial to understand Kant's views on dignity as they have heavily influenced contemporary thought and presuppositions.

For Kant, human dignity is based on our status as rational beings. In particular, in his *Groundwork for the Metaphysics of Morals*, Kant states that "morality, and humanity so far as it is capable of morality, are the only things that have dignity."[7]

So, for Kant, it is not simply the rationality that humans have which demonstrates our dignity, but rather the capacity that rationality gives us to make moral judgements. In particular, Kant is concerned with two things: the status of human beings as ends in themselves, never as means to ends, and their ability to be lawgivers.[8]

For Kant, human beings – by virtue of their humanity – are never to be treated as means to ends. We cannot simply use humanity as a means to getting what we want – and equally, we should not allow others to use our own humanity as means to getting what they want.[9] In particular, for Kant, this means sharing the same ends or aims as others. For instance, if I promise to return the book you lend me, I should keep that promise. In doing so, I share your aim for you to get the book back once I have finished with it. If I make a false promise, however, your aim is different to mine – whilst you intend to get the book back, my aim is to keep it for my own benefit.

In making that false promise, I fail to show respect to your humanity, because I am treating you as a means to my end (of keeping the book).

Why do we owe this respect to human beings as ends in themselves? For Kant, humans are ends in themselves because of their relationship to the moral law. The moral law is something that human beings are, by virtue of pure reason, duty-bound to obey. The moral law is therefore binding – it is not contingent upon additional motives or any desired effects of an action, but is in itself sufficient to obligate any rational person to obey it.[10]

> Humans are both subject to the moral law and givers of the law. In particular, the human will to act morally is not merely subject to the law, but subject to it in such a way that it must be viewed as prescribing the law to itself...the law of which it sees itself as the author.[11]

So, for Kant, an important part of our humanity is that we are both subject to the law and authors of the law itself. Returning to the earlier point that, for Kant, humanity has dignity insofar as it has the capacity for morality, we can see that a fundamental part of Kant's understanding of human dignity is our autonomy – our ability to be givers of the law to which we are at the same time subject.

Are choice and autonomy enough?

If those who advocate assisted dying, following Kant, equate dignity with autonomy and choice, we must consider whether this is an adequate understanding of dignity. This essay will argue that both choice and autonomy are inadequate as indicators of human dignity in themselves.

It is problematic to equate choice, and in particular making the choice to die, with dignity. Consider the definition of a 'dignified death' proposed by Dignity in Dying, which is worth quoting in full here:

— Choice over where we die, who is present and our treatment options.

— Access to expert information on our options, good quality end-of-life care, and support for loved ones and carers.

— Control over how we die, our symptoms and pain relief, and planning our own death.[12]

This definition, for Dignity in Dying, applies to those who, like Jeffrey, are living with life-limiting illnesses such as cancer, heart failure, or motor neurone

Both choice and autonomy are inadequate as indicators of human dignity in themselves.

disease. But this definition could equally be applied by others to a young, relatively physically healthy adult who wanted to end their own life. If a 26-year-old man who struggled with depression and anxiety, or 21-year-old lesbian woman who was struggling to accept her sexuality chose to end their own life, they could according to this definition have a dignified death. They could choose to die in a particular place, on their own if that is their choice; gain information on their options: which methods of suicide are less painful or drawn out than others, and they would certainly have control in choosing the method of suicide.

But who could hear of a case like this and not consider it a tragedy? If either of these people approached us with their plan to take their own life for these reasons, few of us would want to encourage them. The instinctive response for most of us would be to do everything within our power to dissuade them from making this choice.[13]

Some might claim here that, whilst we may consider it a tragedy for either of these people to commit suicide and we may want to discourage them, we would never force them to remain alive against their will. They might argue that, in enabling people to take this option for themselves, we would be respecting their dignity at the very end of their lives.

But can the act of choosing to end one's own life in and of itself alone constitute dignity? Consider the alternative, real-life case of Bernd Brandes: a German engineer who was killed and eaten by another engineer named Armin Meiwes.[14] In 2001, Meiwes had posted an advert online asking for a "young, well-built man who wanted to be eaten", and later discovered Brandes' advert offering "the chance to eat me alive".[15]

The two met one night at Meiwes' home. The account of what happened after that makes for difficult reading. It includes Brandes taking 20 sleeping pills, and Meiwes later stabbing him in the neck before cooking and eating parts of his body.

According to the evidence, Brandes consented to everything that happened to him, and chose to meet Meiwes that night with the intention of being killed and eaten. Meiwes claims that Brandes had planned meticulously exactly how he wanted to die.[16] Yet many of us would struggle to describe the manner of Brandes' death as dignified, and we would be reluctant to encourage anyone contemplating undertaking a similar pursuit. The law agreed that this action was unacceptable – despite Brandes' consent, Meiwes was convicted of murder in 2006.

Clearly it is problematic to assert that a death where the person who dies has choice and control necessarily constitutes a dignified death.

Other human qualities

If autonomy and choice aren't enough in themselves to account for human dignity, some may argue that dignity should be based on other human qualities or capacities. For instance, they might follow Kant in associating human dignity with the capacity for morality.

However, this is problematic for several reasons. Firstly, morality is said to have been observed in various animal species – not just humans. Many species exhibit signs of distress when their companions die, according to primatologist Frans de Waal,[17] and it is claimed that other species show emotions such as love and empathy.[18] Undoubtedly more research is needed, but if non-human animals are shown to be capable of being moral, and dignity is connected with morality for Kant, his claim that dignity is exclusively human cannot stand according to his own definitions.

Those who want to claim that human dignity lies in our capacity for morality also fail to account for the fact that newborn babies are held to have dignity long before they develop the faculties for morality, and those with advanced learning disabilities may struggle (at least to some extent) to make moral choices, yet still have dignity.

Others might argue that human dignity is not based on the human capacity for morality, but rather on some other distinctively human quality, such as our capacity for creativity.[19] This can be said to manifest itself in human innovation – *homo sapiens* is the species that created the aeroplane, built the Eiffel Tower, and invented the World Wide Web. Humans therefore have worth, or value, because of their capacity to create, which is illustrated in these brilliant innovations.

Whilst there is more strength in the claim that this level of creativity is distinctively human, locating dignity in our capacity for innovation is problematic if we are also to claim that dignity is intrinsic to all human beings. Firstly, once again non-human animals show some level of creativity, especially in their use of tools. For instance, at a chimpanzee settlement on the Ivory Coast, stone tools have been found which the chimpanzees are believed to have used to crack nuts.[20]

However, an even more problematic fact is that there are many human beings who are not capable of such innovation, such as those with profound physical or learning disabilities, and those who have advanced cognitive decline, for example people with dementia. This is particularly problematic if dignity is attributed to those at the end of life, as there are growing numbers of people with dementia.[21] Many people who are at the end of life are in the later stages of dementia – indeed, dementia is now the leading cause of death in England and Wales.[22] Any account of human dignity at the end of life must therefore be able to include people with dementia.

It is clear, then, that we cannot claim both that all human beings, including those at the end of life, have dignity, and that this is a result of our capacities, whether they be autonomy, creativity, or morality.

We must consider what alternative accounts can adequately encapsulate what it means to have human dignity.

1   Paul Byrne, 'A final family meal and then 16 hours later tragic dad ends his
    life at assisted suicide clinic', *The Mirror, www.mirror.co.uk/news/uk-news/final-
    family-meal-16-hours-5762674#rlabs=8*, accessed 24 July 2016.

2   Ibid.

3   Dignitas, Principles/Philosophy, *www.dignitas.ch/index.php?option=com_
    content&view=article&id=10&Itemid=46&lang=en*, accessed 5 Nov 2016.

4   *www.dignityindying.org.uk/about-us/*, accessed 24 July 2016.

5   Assisted Dying (No 2) Bill, Hansard, HC vol. 599, col 656 (11 September
    2015) *hansard.parliament.uk/Commons/2015-09-11/debates/15091126000003/
    AssistedDying(No2)Bill*, accessed 5 Nov 2016.

6   The association between dignity and worth is explored further in chapter 2.

7   Kant, *Groundwork for the Metaphysic of Morals*, trans. Jonathan Bennett.
    www.earlymoderntexts.com/assets/pdfs/kant1785.pdf, accessed 14 Aug 2016.

8   Those familiar with Kant's *Groundwork* will also recognise his concern with the
    principle of universalisability of moral maxims. I have chosen not to focus on
    this here as it does not seem to be germane to his concept of dignity.

9   JE Hare, *God and Morality: A Philosophical History* (Malden, MA: Blackwell
    Publishing, 2007), p. 149.

10 Kant, *Groundwork*, pp. 2-10.

11 Ibid., p. 31.

12 *www.dignityindying.org.uk/about-us/*, accessed 24 July 2016.

13 Indeed, the writers of Coronation Street were careful not to be seen to
    encourage any form of suicide, carefully following advice from organisations
    such as Samaritans. For instance, they deliberately avoided showing what
    substances were in the liquid that Hayley drank, or how they had been
    acquired.

14 With thanks to Nigel Biggar who first made me aware of the relevance of this
    case to the assisted dying debate in seminars at the University of Oxford, 2012
    and 2013.

15 Roisin O'Connor, 'Armin Meiwes: Interview with a Cannibal documentary
    sheds new light on one of Germany's most infamous murderers' *The
    Independent*, 9 Feb 2016 *www.independent.co.uk/news/world/europe/armin-meiwes-
    interview-with-a-cannibal-documentary-sheds-new-light-on-one-of-germany-s-most-
    infamous-a6863201.html*, accessed 24 July 2016.

16 DOCS: Interview With A Cannibal, *www.youtube.com/watch?v=ym6TWmXw_fE*,
    accessed 24 July 2016. Please note: this video will auto-play and is explicit from
    the start.

[17] Brigitte Osterath, 'Do animals mourn their dead?' *Deutsche Welle*, *www.dw.com/en/do-animals-mourn-their-dead/a-19564029*, accessed 21 May 17].

[18] Tia Ghose, 'Animals Are Moral Creatures, Scientist Argues', *www.livescience.com/24802-animals-have-morals-book.html*, accessed 14 Aug 2016.

[19] cf. eg. R Keith Sawyer, *Explaining Creativity: The Science of Human Innovation* (Oxford: Oxford University Press, 2012).

[20] *news.bbc.co.uk/1/hi/sci/tech/6356773.stm,* accessed 5 Nov 2016.

[21] Alzheimer's Society, 'Facts for the media', *www.alzheimers.org.uk/site/scripts/documents_info.php?documentID=535&pageNumber=2,* accessed 14 Aug 2016.

[22] BBC News, 'Dementia now leading cause of death', 14 Nov 2016, *www.bbc.co.uk/news/health-37972141*, accessed 27 Dec 2016.

2
Understanding dignity

We have seen that proponents of assisted dying often associate making this choice with dignity. We have also argued that choice and autonomy cannot in themselves adequately account for what human dignity is. Dignity has, however, been understood in other ways, to which we turn in this chapter.

As discussed in the previous chapter, the origins of 'dignity' are in the Latin word *dignitas*, from *dignus*, meaning 'worthy'. To understand the use of dignity and its relationship to 'worth', it will help to examine how it has been used historically and the different senses in which this 'worth' is interpreted. In his book on dignity, Michael Rosen demonstrates three particular dimensions of the historical use of this term: high social status (honour), behaviour worthy of respect, and intrinsic value.[1]

In antiquity, the use of dignity seemed to be associated with high social status. Cicero equated the term with honour: notably, honour that is only attributable to humans, on account of our rational nature. As a result of this rational nature, which renders us superior to animals, Cicero argued that "sensual pleasure is wholly unworthy of the dignity of the human race".[2]

The use of the term to mean honour continued into early Christianity, with Pope Gelasius I using it to refer to the social status of Emperor Anastasius in 494. In his letter to the emperor, Gelasius wrote, "[you] take precedence over all mankind in dignity", but added, "nevertheless you piously bow the neck to those who have charge of divine affairs and seek from them the means of your salvation."[3]

A second but related use of the term can be found in the writings of the Elizabethan philosopher and statesman Francis Bacon. He published a Latin translation of his own book *On the Advancement of Learning*, with the title *De Dignitate et Augmentis Scientiarum*. In doing this, Bacon attributed dignity to a particular pursuit: learning. In this sense, it is a certain worthiness or respect that belongs to particular behaviours. Throughout the text there are references to dignity, which he clearly associated with worth, such as when he stated "our intent is to balance the dignity of knowledge in the scale with other things, and to estimate their true values according to universal testimony."[4] In this second dimension of the term, there is a respect that is not due to persons by virtue of a particular status, but rather one that is commanded by engaging in particular pursuits.

A third dimension of the relationship between dignity and worth is the concept of intrinsic worth, which is found in Kant's writings. For Kant, the dignity (*Würde*) of human beings is something that is intrinsic to them. However, it is not based on their place in creation, but rather on their status as rational beings. As we saw in the previous chapter, this rational capacity is the quality that enables a human being to be both subject to, and a giver of, the moral law. For Kant, the law itself is supreme and commands respect.[5] Humans, as givers of the law, are ends in themselves, and are therefore also worthy of respect:

> *Rational beings are called 'persons', because their nature already marks them out as ends in themselves (i.e. as not to be used merely as means)—which makes such a being an object of respect.[6]*

As we saw in the previous chapter, basing dignity on 'human' capacity is problematic as it can both include some animals, and exclude some human beings. Instead, we would argue that the most satisfactory account of dignity is that all humans, *irrespective of their abilities or cognitive capacity*, are possessed of an inalienable dignity. To explain how this can be grounded, we turn to Christian theology.

Dignity in Christian theology

The dignity of humanity is a central concept in Christian thought, especially in the teaching of the Catholic Church. The *Compendium of Social Doctrine of the Church*, for instance, claims that "the whole of the Church's social doctrine, in fact, develops from the principle that affirms the inviolable dignity of the human person."[7]

How does Christianity account for this inviolable dignity? Catholicism, in particular, grounds it in the fact that humans are made in the image of God. The Catechism of the Catholic Church states that "the dignity of the human person is rooted in his creation in the image and likeness of God".[8] This idea is expanded upon in the US Catholic Bishops' *Pastoral Letter on Catholic Social Teaching and the U.S. Economy*. The letter talks about the church's "vision of the transcendent worth – the sacredness – of human beings" and argues that

> *when we deal with each other, we should do so with the sense of awe that arises in the presence of something holy and sacred. For that is what human beings are: we are created in the image of God (Gen 1:27).*[9]

But if we are to understand how being made in the image of God demonstrates the worth of human beings, we firstly need to ask what exactly being created in the image of God means. We will look at three possible explanations of this, which have been identified and named as the 'substantive', 'functional' and 'relational' images in *Wholly Living*, a joint publication of Theos, Cafod and Tearfund.[10] These three interpretations are not necessarily mutually exclusive – human beings may be understood to bear the image of God in all three of these senses.

The substantive image interpretation argues that being made in the image of God means sharing in some of his substantial characteristics. These might include, for example, sharing in the divine capacity for reason or intellect.[11] This is consistent with the understanding of God as rational, and the description of the *Logos* of God in the prologue to John's Gospel (John 1:1-18) – a word that is related to Greek concepts of thinking, considering and reasoning (*logizomai*) – not just 'speaking'.

However, the biblical story testifies to other more distinctive qualities of the God of the Old and New Testaments, especially creativity and productivity. Those following a substantive interpretation may instead see human beings as sharing in the nature of the God who created the universe through our own creative abilities. The image and likeness of God, according to this interpretation, is therefore shown in certain human characteristics and capacities such as reason, intellect and creativity.

The functional image interpretation argues that, as humans are made in the image of God, they have a particular job to do – namely, caring for, tending to, and subduing the earth and creatures within it. This reflects the descriptions of the creation stories in Genesis 1 and Genesis 2:

> *So God created humankind in his image...God blessed them, and God said to them, 'Be fruitful and multiply, and fill the earth and subdue it; and have dominion over the fish of the sea and over the birds of the air and over every living thing that moves upon the earth. (Gen. 1:27-8)*

> *The Lord God took the man and put him in the garden of Eden to till it and keep it. (Gen. 2:15)*

Human beings therefore bear the image of God by caring for his creation. As Rowan Williams puts it:

> *The creation stories of Genesis 1 and 2 see the creation of humanity as quite specifically the creation of an agent, a person, who can care for and protect the animal world, reflecting the care of God himself who enjoys the goodness of what he has made.[12]*

According to this interpretation, human beings therefore bear the image of God not simply by having certain qualities, but by actively fulfilling certain functions. Bearing the image of God is demonstrated in what we do – namely in caring for God's creation.

The relational image interpretation argues that being made in the image of God means existing in relationship to God, as well as to other human beings (and the rest of creation) in a way that reflects something of God's own relational nature. The relational nature of God is fundamental to the doctrine of the Trinity. God the Father, God the Son, and God the Holy Spirit all exist in dynamic relationship with one another.[13]

Pope Benedict XVI's encyclical *Caritas in Veritate* argued for relationships as essential to what it means to be human:

> *As a spiritual being the human creature is defined through interpersonal relations. The more authentically he or she lives these relations, the more his or her own personal identity matures.[14]*

To bear the image of God as human beings is therefore to reflect his relational nature in our relationships with God and with other people.

Each of these interpretations (substantive, functional and relational) is valid – but how do they demonstrate the inalienable worth of human beings? It is problematic to argue that humans have worth through using their various capacities to reflect the nature of God: to reason and be creative, to care for creation, and to show love to others, because we run into the same problem as Kantian interpretations of human dignity previously mentioned, making dignity contingent upon human abilities. If this is the case, those who may lack the mental faculties for these, and indeed all human beings, are excluded to some extent. We all fail to behave rationally at times; some of us may be less creative than others; and we may all at times fail in our duty to tend to the earth – whether through our role in polluting the atmosphere, or in overconsumption, or using products for which animals have been treated cruelly. And every human being is guilty of failing to show love at times when they could, whether intentionally or simply through negligence or absent-mindedness.

But this is not, in fact, what Christians argue. Being made in the image of God is not a quality that human beings can either have or have not, or possess in varying degrees. We are simply made in the image of God as a fact. We are created in the image of God, irrespective of our ability or success in making that image manifest. Indeed, all human beings fail to make this image fully manifest, as it is marred in all of us.

Fundamentally, "Humans are not creatures that are valued by God because they bear the *imago dei*. Humans are creatures that bear the *imago dei* because they are valued by God."[15] This places the dignity of human beings, in particular, in a relational context: we are made in the image of God because we are valued by God. This is illustrated well in Psalm 8, where the psalmist asks, "What are human beings that you are mindful of them,/mortals that you care for them?" before observing, "Yet you have made them a little lower than God,/and crowned them with glory and honour." (Psalm 8:4-5) The psalmist here shows us the connection between the worth, and status – some might say dignity – of human beings, and the fact that God cares for us.

The connection between worth and being cared for somewhat challenges our modern notions of value. When asked to think of valuable items we might name an expensive sports car, a Rolex watch, or a MacBook Pro. Certainly, these items have monetary value. But if someone who owned one of these was burgled, or lost them in an accident or fire, what would be the real cause of their suffering? They may be able to replace them through an insurance claim – but this would not undo the suffering caused by losing things that were important to them. By the same token those who lose less expensive items with more sentimental value often make public pleas that the items are worth very little in monetary terms, but are priceless because of the meaning they have for the owner.

This is illustrated well in the analogy of a child's teddy bear. It may be torn, battered, and certainly incapable of performing any function. Yet for that child, the teddy bear may be completely irreplaceable.[16] Some people or families might have pets that look unappealing, are unable to perform any kind of tricks, and may by many standards seem worth very little, yet their value may be immeasurable to their owner. Such analogies steer us towards the idea that dignity resides not in the thing itself but in the fact that it is loved. And humans, according to Christian thought, are fundamentally and inalienably loved by God.

Dignity, worth and the end of life

We saw in the previous chapter that 'dignity' has been taken (or assumed) by many advocates of assisted dying to mean choice, independence and control, especially in the context of the end of life. However, our explorations of the origins of the term have suggested that a more adequate understanding of dignity is an inalienable worth attributable to all human beings irrespective of their capacities. The Christian account argues that this is based on being loved and valued by the God who made us in his image.

But Christian theology does not have a monopoly on the view of human beings as valued and therefore dignified and nor would Christian thinkers claim to. Indeed, as we saw above, the relational image interpretation of the *imago Dei* highlights that the relationships between people – not just those with God – reflect the relational nature of God. Our worth is not just shown in being valued by God, but in being valued by any human being: a friend, a family member or partner, or even a stranger on the street.

This worth is not dependent on an assumption that all human beings have an abundance of loving, supportive relationships. A lonely homeless person may be estranged from their family or feel like they are without friends, but they may still be valued by the person who buys them a sandwich, or the charity worker who offers them a room in a hostel, or the person who simply stops to greet them and acknowledge their humanity. If all humans have this inalienable relational worth, being valued by another human being is therefore significant, because we are deemed to have worth by other beings of equal value.

Having argued that true dignity consists in this inalienable relational worth, and is demonstrated in being valued by others, we must now consider what it means for people at the end of life to have this. If we argue that it is not demonstrated through them having choice and control over how and when they die, we must show what it means for dignity as inalienable relational worth to be honoured at the end of life. What does a dignified death – in this sense of the word dignity – look like?

1   Michael Rosen, *Dignity: Its History and Meaning* (Cambridge, MA & London, England: Harvard University Press, 2012), pp. 13-31.

2   Cicero, *De Officiis*, cited in Rosen, *Dignity*, p. 12.

3   cited in Rosen, *Dignity*, p. 13.

4   Sir Francis Bacon, 'On the Advancement of Learning', *oll.libertyfund.org/titles/ bacon-the-advancement-of-learning*, accessed 21 May 2017.

5   Kant, *Groundwork for the Metaphysic of Morals*, trans. Jonathan Bennett. *www. earlymoderntexts.com/assets/pdfs/kant1785.pdf*, accessed 14 Aug 2016, p. 27.

6   Kant, *Groundwork*, p. 29.

7   Compendium of the Social Doctrine of the Church, 107, *www.vatican.va/roman_ curia/pontifical_councils/justpeace/documents/rc_pc_justpeace_doc_20060526_ compendio-dott-soc_en.html*, accessed 20 Aug 2016.

8   *Catechism of the Catholic Church*, Part Three: Life in Christ, Section One: Man's Vocation Life in the Spirit, Chapter One: The Dignity of the Human Person, *www.vatican.va/archive/ccc_css/archive/catechism/p3s1c1.htm*, accessed 27 Nov 2016.

9   Economic Justice for All: Pastoral Letter on Catholic Social Teaching and the U.S. Economy, *www.usccb.org/upload/economic_justice_for_all.pdf*, p. 8, accessed 20 Aug 2016.

10 Theos, *Wholly Living: A New Perspective on International Development* (London: Theos, 2010), pp. 24-6.

11 J Wentzel van Huyssteen, *Alone in the World? Human Uniqueness in Science and Theology* (Grand Rapids: William B. Eerdmans Publishing Company, 2006), p.126.

12 Rowan Williams, Operation Noah Annual Lecture 2009, *operationnoah.org/ resources/operation-noah-annual-lecture-2009-rowan-williams/*, accessed 27 Nov 2016.

13 This idea is explored by a number of theologians, e.g., 'John Milbank on the Trinity in a Postmodern Age' in A. McGrath (ed.), *The Christian Theology Reader*, 4th edn. (Chichester: Wiley-Blackwell, 2011), p. 209-11.

14 Caritas in Veritate, *w2.vatican.va/content/benedict-xvi/en/encyclicals/documents/ hf_ben-xvi_enc_20090629_caritas-in-veritate.html*, accessed 27 Nov 2016.

15 A Ritchie and N Spencer, *The Case for Christian Humanism* (London: Theos, 2014), p. 52.

16 Ritchie & Spencer, *Humanism*, p. 50.

3
Dignity at the end of life

We have argued that true human dignity is best realised and honoured when people are valued by others, rather than simply when people have choice, control and independence. It is now important to understand the implications of this for the assisted dying debate. What does it mean to truly honour people's dignity at the end of life?

To understand this question we interviewed a range of healthcare professionals, all of whom have extensive experience of working with people approaching the end of life.[1] The professionals were a combination of doctors and consultants (including specialists in end of life care), nurses and chaplains. To ensure a variety of perspectives, we spoke to people in those roles who had experience in a range of settings, including hospitals, hospices, and community care. Some of the professionals held religious faith (including Roman Catholic and Protestant), while others did not.[2]

Importantly, there was also a range of views amongst these professionals on the issue of assisted dying. Some supported a change in the law, others opposed a change, and others were undecided. In all cases the professionals had, unsurprisingly, nuanced and balanced views on the issue: those who opposed a change in the law were often still sympathetic to those who wanted to choose assisted dying, whilst those who supported a change in the law were nonetheless conscious of the complexity of this issue.

In this chapter we will explore the insights gained from these interviews with professionals, firstly in relation to the key elements of what it means for a person to die with dignity, and secondly regarding the implications of this for the assisted dying debate. We will conclude from these interviews, and broader evidence including articles and policy reports, that truly dignified dying demands relationships in which the dying person and those important to him or her are truly and deeply valued. We will also conclude that through these relationships, the main concerns that lead people to consider assisted dying can either be alleviated or refuted.

Dignified dying

In chapter 2 we saw that the organisation Dignity in Dying argues that choice and control, including over how and when we die, are essential for a dignified death. Yet all of the professionals interviewed, whatever their views on assisted dying, testified that most of the people they had cared for had had dignified deaths even without this kind of choice being available to them.

So what *is* necessary for a dignified death? As we argued in the previous chapter, relationships are essential for honouring people's dignity, and when caring for people at the end of life, the existence of such relationships *that value the person for everything they are and have been* is essential. The professionals we interviewed emphasised this point throughout our conversations:

> *I think a lot of [having a good death] is being held in relationship – knowing you're loved as you go. (Interview 3: Doctor)*

> *A lot of what I'm doing [is showing], "You are important. What you say is really important. Your life has been of value." (Interview 4: Chaplain)*

There are a number of ways in which professionals said they valued the people they were caring for. Key among these was listening to and understanding the person as a person, not simply as a patient. This is central to the phenomenon of person-centred health and social care, where professionals recognise the need to understand the patient as a person with their own background, history, needs and wishes. This person-centred approach was evidently essential for all of the professionals we spoke to, as part of their relationship with the people they were caring for:

> *I think part of the dignity, for me, is...not treating them just as a patient; treating them as an individual, getting to know them as an individual, understanding who they are and where they come from, and knowing a bit more about them. (Interview 11: Nurse)*

> *I think that's...especially important...in end of life care... people know when they're loved, and they know when they're valued...I think sometimes just...the continuity of presence, backwards and forwards, seeing them, every time you're in popping and saying hello. It's almost saying, "You've not been forgotten." (Interview 4: Chaplain)*

There are a number of ways in which professionals said they valued the people they were caring for. Key among these was listening to and understanding the person as a person, not simply as a patient.

Listening to people approaching the end of life had practical benefits. By understanding them better, professionals could understand the kinds of things they needed and asked for, and relate them to what they knew about the person. For instance, one nurse mentioned caring for a number of ex-military men, many of whom fought in World War II, who want to be smart, shave every day, and keep up the kind of presentation and appearance that had been their habit. It was important to understand this, in contrast to, for example, teenagers and young adults with life-limiting conditions, who may care less about smart appearance and more about being able to laugh and joke with their friends.

This demonstrates what is at the core of person-centred care: understanding the person and thereby understanding their needs, wishes and preferences at the end of life. All of the professionals interviewed saw it as a part of their role to understand what was important to the person at the end of life. They expressed this in different ways, including "respecting the wishes of the person who is dying", "[finding out] what's important to them, what's helped them to cope in life up till now", "[finding out] what they feel is them as a person and what they need to feel as good as they can about themselves and about the situation at that time", and "respecting the person that they are, and realising that they are still a person, they've still got wants and wishes."

Clearly finding out what is important to the person, and honouring this as far as possible, is a significant part of valuing them as a person with inalienable relational worth at the end of life. This depends on all the professionals involved in their care respecting them for who they are, rather than treating them simply as medical cases.

Also, as we saw in the previous chapter, human nature is inherently relational – and this is no less true when a person is at the end of life. This was conveyed most strikingly in a photograph of David Kirby, who became a symbol of the AIDS epidemic when his photo was featured on the cover of LIFE Magazine in November 1990.[3] In this poignant photograph, the suffering of David's family at his bedside is patent. The experience of David's dying was clearly also the experience of the people who loved him.

It is important to note that a person will have relationships that may come in a number of forms – this may include family, but could be, for example, a person's partner, friends, neighbours, religious communities, former work colleagues, and fellow members of special interest or peer support groups (including online forums).

It is important that professionals caring for a person approaching the end of life honour these relationships, again by listening to and valuing those who matter to the person at the end of life, who make up their network of relationships. The professionals we interviewed clearly regarded getting to know those who are important to the person as part of their job too:

> Quite often as we are supporting the patient or the family through these decisions...you do find out little bits about them... and I think that's where I get my love of the job from...you get to know the person, and you get to know those that are important to them. (Interview 10: Nurse)

They testified to the difference that valuing these people could make to the person having a good death:

> It's less easy to have a good death if the family[4] is feeling abandoned, isolated, with a sense of crisis, trauma. (Interview 5: Doctor)

> In reality, it's the tiny things, day to day, that make the difference. Getting to know someone, their family. (Interview 8: Doctor)

One doctor emphasised that the people who matter to the dying person should be included as part of the process, not simply an afterthought:

Families are an important part of the process...to make sure that they are on board with the patient's wishes, ideally as part of a unified group of people who are talking about all the same things at the same time. (Interview 2: Doctor)

People are more likely to have a better experience at the end of life if those who matter to them are also involved in the process. This is because in many cases, the happiness of those people is also important to the dying person. However, some of the professionals interviewed also pointed out that at times there may be conflict between the expressed wishes of the dying person and those around them.

Such cases raise difficult questions. One chaplain told us about a dying person who made arrangements for her funeral with him, which would involve him conducting the service. The person died soon after this and the chaplain only then discovered, after speaking to the person's family, that they did not want the chaplain to be involved in the funeral. In that situation, the chaplain felt it was important to recognise the needs of the family in their grief:

We ended up saying, "Well...as her husband, her family, your needs are important too, so we're able to let go of those previous arrangements." And it was the dignity of how the family were dealing with that that mattered...you have to...respect that dignity goes beyond the wishes of the person sometimes. (Interview 9: Chaplain)

The chaplain said some prayers with the family which helped partly to meet the wishes that the dying person had expressed. But in the situation of the family's bereavement, he was able to recognise the importance of the family's dignity. We must, therefore, bear in mind that, whilst the wishes of the person at the end of life should be considered first, the wishes and needs of those important to them must also be regarded as important, and may (with sufficient reason) in certain cases take precedence.

Having recognised this, we must now consider in more detail what matters to people at the end of life. What is important to them, to enable them to have a dignified death? Although each person's wishes and needs are, of course, individual, there are certain common themes that emerged from our interviews with professionals. Many of these are also reported in *What's important to me,* a national review of the choices that people

> **Relationships with professionals and others are central to enabling a person to have a dignified death.**

want at the end of life, which was published in February 2015 following a public engagement exercise with over 1,000 people.[5] Together with the findings from our interviews, they give an important insight into what truly matters to people at the end of life.

The findings considered here relate to key aspects of people's needs at the end of life: psychological, social, emotional, and spiritual. These are the four elements of 'total pain' at the end of life identified by Dame Cicely Saunders, founder of the modern hospice movement, which shaped the modern understanding of palliative care.[6] Meeting needs in all four of these aspects of a person's experience were also identified in *What's important to me.*[7]

Meeting all of these needs depends on professionals valuing the person at the end of life and those important to them, to ensure these wishes are met. It will be evident that relationships with professionals and others are central to enabling a person to have a dignified death.

Acceptance

The most frequently recurring theme in the interviews with professionals was that acceptance was important for a person to have a good and dignified death.

> *In abstract terms, a good death is a combination of understanding, acceptance, and peace. (Interview 8: Doctor)*

This acceptance was not just about the person's mental state of happiness, but also had an impact on physical symptoms at the end of life:

> *The patients that don't kind of get their heads around where they are in their disease process and that can't really accept that they're dying often suffer a lot more agitation and can be more difficult to manage symptomatically...but the people who are able to...talk about what's going on, and be in some way...at peace with what's going on, tend to have less in the way of agitation and symptoms. (Interview 1: Doctor)*

For people to accept their own death, they depend in part on professionals to communicate to them that they are approaching the end of life (insofar as this is consistent with their wishes) – something which many of the professionals we spoke to pointed out. One doctor told us about his experiences as a trainee several decades ago of a shocking failure to communicate openly with a dying person:

*One of the very first patients I visited...[was] a man with
terminal lung cancer, and he didn't know what was wrong with
him, and didn't know what his circumstances were...and...I said,
"Isn't it his business? Shouldn't he be told what's going on – in
kindly terms?"...A retired matron [was]...taking charge of the
situation, and she said, "A patient with cancer should never be
told what's wrong with them." (Interview 2: Doctor)*

We would hope that such instances are much less common
today. However, a number of the professionals nonetheless
mentioned the need for more honest and open communication
about dying. This is one of the Priorities for Care of the Dying
Person set out in *One chance to get it right*[8] – the approach to
caring for dying people published in response to the review
and phasing out of the Liverpool Care Pathway.[9] It is essential
that those who wish to know when they are approaching the
end of life are communicated with openly to ensure they can
come to a place of acceptance about their dying.

Acceptance of death also has practical implications
for treatment. One doctor observed that some healthcare
professionals continue to pursue treatments when it is clear
that the person is dying, and the patient would be able to
have a better, more peaceful death, if their care focussed
on comfort. This risks the person dying in the anonymity of
hospital instead of in more comfortable and more personal
surroundings.

However, even when professionals have accepted and
communicated that a person is dying, it can be very difficult
for some people to accept their situation. The professionals
we spoke to mentioned tragic instances where people had not
accepted what was happening to them:

>*I think some of the worst deaths are when people are striving and desperately trying not to die, and feeling 'this is all so unfair'. (Interview 3: Doctor)*

In contrast, when people were able to accept that they were dying, this made a huge difference to their death:

>*I'm reminded of a patient who was a young-ish man (I think he was late fifties) – and I told him he had, you know, not long to live, and he said, "Well, doc, you know, I've had a good life – I've seen my children grow up". And I was really struck by his peace. (Interview 3: Doctor)*

As we have observed, the dying process also includes the people who are important to the person. In some cases, the person themselves was not the one who struggled to accept their impending death, but those around them. Some professionals mentioned that this was even the case in some cases where a person was dying in their eighties or nineties, at a time when death would be more expected:

>*I had a woman who was nearly 90 – and her husband was absolutely stricken that she was going to die. And I said to her, 'Well, had you thought about dying before?' And her head went up very quickly and she looked me in the eye, and she said, 'No, not really – of course I haven't thought about dying!' (Interview 3: Doctor)*

Such a powerful example demonstrates the support that many need to come to accept that they are dying – even at a time when it should not come as a surprise. Through a combination of good communication and supportive attitudes, professionals caring for a person at the end of life can help them to accept their own death, enabling them to develop peace of mind as a first step towards dying with dignity.

Dying in peace

Sometimes, however, people who have accepted their impending deaths still do not experience peace of mind in their final days and weeks. Professionals spoke of people who had received all of the medical care they required but were still agitated as they approached death. They reported a number of reasons for this. In some cases, the issue was simply missing what was comfortable and familiar to them.

> *It was coming up to a Christmas a few years ago...and a gentleman was close to death. He was unconscious, but he was incredibly agitated, and they'd given him the maximum dose of the particular medication that he could have, and it wasn't touching him. So...[I talked] to his family and found out that he had been a church organist...I grabbed a CD of carols from a cathedral...and genuinely, within half an hour of the music being put on, his agitation had gone completely. And he died very peacefully a couple of hours later. (Interview 6: Chaplain)*

The effect of something as simple as playing familiar music here is profound. However, for some people, there are deeper problems, such as unresolved issues with people who are important to them:

> *[I see] families who've been estranged for a few years. If you actually get these people to a point where they'll have the conversation with you, you'll be surprised how many will say to you, "You know what, I haven't spoken to my son or my daughter or whatever for [ten years], and it would just be nice to have one more conversation with them, so I could say this or this". And things like that are easy to do...if you get the consent and you get the people...a phone call nowadays or...with computers...it can make such a difference. (Interview 11: Nurse)*

The nurse who told us this added that when people have this kind of angst and a professional can do something to change it, "it changes their perspective on it, and it's something that stays with you forever."

In some cases, the issues on people's minds as they approached the end of life were not so much about unresolved tension or estrangement, but more practical.

I think...older wives tend to worry about how their husbands are going to cope...perhaps he hasn't done the cooking before, or around the house - they worry about the practical things... Some of the men I've spoken to worry about how their wives - again - are going to deal with the finances, cause they've always sorted the finances out...[they're] trying to protect one another. (Interview 4: Chaplain)

One of the most memorable deaths I can remember was a chap who...the thing that he was worried about the most was how his wife was going to sort out the finances afterwards, and just the simple act of bringing in someone that was a welfare and benefits advisor, and being able to sit down with him for half an hour...and say, "Don't you worry, this is what's going to happen, we're going to put this support in for your wife..." From that moment on, that man physically, you could almost see him relax, and from that point on, his process to the end of his life was a different journey for him. (Interview 11: Nurse)

It is important to remember, as observed earlier, that the people who are important to someone are often not just relatives:

I can remember one chap who, the one thing that was stressing him more than anything else, he was the treasurer for his bowls club, and he just needed to get some money paid into

the...club's account. And once that was done, he was a different
fellow, he was like, "Thank goodness for that, I can relax now."
(Interview 11: Nurse)

Once again, we can see clearly the profound impact that a
person's relationships can have on their experience of dying. In
some cases, people may not be estranged, or have unresolved
personal or practical issues, but simply want to see a person
they love again. There may be practical reasons why they are
not able to see that person easily – for instance, if they live far
away:

It seems to [happen a lot] – I mean sometimes people hang
on, and you think..."We can't believe that they're still here". And
it's like they're waiting for somebody to come, and then when
that person comes, it's like, "Right, I can go now." (Interview 6:
Chaplain)

Clearly the people who are important to someone can be
essential to their peace at the end of life. When a person is able
to die in peace, professionals testify that the effect is striking:

[Often] the person has slipped away in their sleep, no trauma,
the environment was tranquil...in fact, the question often is,
"Have they died?" because it's that slipping away... (Interview 5:
Doctor)

Controlling pain and other symptoms

Having seen the profound effect of a person's mental
state (in terms of acceptance and peace) on their dying, it is
nonetheless true that physical aspects of their death have
a significant effect too. The experience of pain in particular
can feature prominently in a person's experience of dying. A
volunteer on a palliative care ward in a Belgian hospice has
written a book with accounts of his experiences. He quotes one

of the people on the ward, Mireille, who had Motor Neurone Disease, and for whom pain treatment had not managed to relieve all pain: "This disease is taking hold of me...The pain lives in me and it's dehumanizing me."[10]

A number of professionals mentioned the importance of being pain-free to people at the end of life:

Most people say they want to be pain-free, that they want to be...rested, sleeping, they want to slip away in their sleep. (Interview 1: Doctor)

A lot of the time [bad deaths] are around the symptoms, pain, the sickness...most people are frightened of dying in pain. (Interview 10: Nurse)

A number of other symptoms clearly worry people about dying, including breathlessness, and urinary and faecal incontinence. However, the professionals were clear that for the most part, such symptoms could be managed. Sometimes the management of pain in a particular case depended on the sensitivity and care of the professional – usually when a person was no longer able to communicate verbally that they were in pain:

You can tell if somebody is in pain, even if they're not conscious. You can tell if they're agitated, and you can give drugs to alleviate those things (and often that's through a syringe driver so that they've got a regular supply of drugs that they need going in, to keep them in a peaceful place). (Interview 6: Chaplain)

If someone is unable to tell us if they're in pain, we try and look for those non-verbal signs of pain – grimacing, rubbing of tummies, anything that might give us an idea, and if we think there is a possibility of pain, then we would give pain relief, because...the last thing we would want is for them to have that pain. (Interview 10: Nurse)

It's really noticing the clues, because sometimes people are in pain and they won't always want to tell you that... (Interview 4: Chaplain)

Some of the professionals pointed out that managing a person's pain was not the end goal, but rather a necessary step to ensuring that they could be peaceful and focus on other issues such as reflecting on their life or preparing practically for death.

"

It does help to be pain free in order to get your act together before you die. (Interview 9: Chaplain)

You need to manage the pain aspects of their illness and their eventual death as best as you can. I think if you get that part right, it means there's a little bit more space

For the few people for whom this wasn't possible, professionals told us that this hadn't always prevented a dignified death.

emotionally or psychologically for the people, then for...resolving their spiritual or psychological concerns. (Interview 11: Nurse)

Sadly, despite the importance of pain relief, it was not possible in every circumstance to ensure a completely pain-free death. However, for the few people for whom this wasn't possible, professionals told us that this hadn't always prevented a dignified death:

I've seen people who've had a good death but have never been completely pain free...it's about them being ready and prepared. (Interview 11: Nurse)

Nonetheless it is important to be realistic about the fact that a few deaths are tragically difficult for the person and those around them, where symptoms could not be completely managed. In such cases, it becomes imperative professionals control absolutely everything that they can to minimise the person's suffering as far as possible:

> *Some deaths just aren't ever going to be good. You know, you have people who have for example a stomach cancer, and they have...a big bleed at the end of their life, and that can be quite traumatic, especially for families...I guess it's making the death as good as it can be for that person, not that we can take away everything that's happening, because we can't control what the disease is doing. We're just trying to minimise the distress around those kind of events as much as we can. (Interview 1: Doctor)*

Respecting the wishes of the person at the end of life is very important, and in perhaps rare instances, some people do not want the pain relief we might expect.

> *I can think of a Buddhist patient that I know, who really wanted the minimum possible pain relief, and wanted to be as conscious as possible for what was going on, and that was part of her philosophy of life. (Interview 7: Chaplain)*

Respecting these wishes is part of meeting not just the person's physical needs. By either relieving people's pain to leave them freer to contemplate other matters, or by respecting their wishes to be in a state where they are alert and not protected from pain, professionals can also support their psychological, social and spiritual needs, too.

Spiritual needs

The concepts of 'spiritual' and 'religious' needs have become increasingly distinct within care settings, such that 'spiritual' care is not just for 'the religious'. Interviewees told us that many people considered religious rituals important to them as they reached the end of life.

> *There have been a few [cases], in my experience, of people who have drifted away from the church, and God, in life, and slowly through the dying process have come to realise how important that might be. So they've been involved in what I call reconciliation...[that] can make a big difference to a good death for them. (Interview 9: Chaplain)*

> *It's happened quite a few times, that people have received communion, or anointing, or whatever they ask for, and this gives them a great sense of peace. (Interview 9: Chaplain)*

For many people, whether they have a religion or not, it is important to plan their funeral. In some cases, making these plans was also important for the person's peace of mind at the end of life:

> *We had one lady who, when she knew that there was no more active treatment that could be done, and that it was only a matter of weeks probably, asked to see me. And she said, 'Right, I want to plan my funeral'. So we talked round it...and I gave her a service book and a hymn book so she could...choose hymns and prayers and things. I...spent a few hours with her on the Sunday, [her local vicar] came to see her on the Thursday, and she died on the Friday, because...it was all sorted, she knew what was going to happen, her mind was at ease. (Interview 6: Chaplain)*

Spiritual and religious needs are therefore important to many people at the end of life and should not be overlooked.

Dying in a place of choice

For many people, where they are at the end of life is an important issue. *What's important to me* identified 'I want to be cared for and die in a place of my choice' as a key theme in people's responses to the review. Similarly, it featured prominently in our interviews with professionals, who told us that place of choice was a key concern for many of the people they had cared for.

As we might expect, people most wanted to be at home, although there were a number of other settings where people sometimes preferred to be.

The professionals we spoke to were clear that they would always try to meet a person's wishes around this where possible. However, it was important to be realistic about when this was not possible, or could potentially mean that the person's other needs were compromised. For instance, sometimes people want to die at home but it would be difficult for them to access the care they need at home. This could be for a number of reasons – because their needs are especially complex, for example, or simply because they are unfortunate enough to be living in an area where there aren't enough services available for people in the community. People may therefore in some cases benefit more from being in a care home or even hospital:

> *Lots of people will say they want to die at home until they're getting towards the end of life, and then they realise actually how difficult that is to be kept pain-free, well supported, and the family being supported as well, when there's limited resources in the community. (Interview 11: Nurse)*

> *I think if [a person's death] happens in a care home, or a hospital, you do tend to get that sense of peacefulness,*

tranquillity, if for no other reason than that the pain relief is there, and the nurse's presence is reassuring...you get better deaths than people might expect. (Interview 5: Doctor)

For many people, their desire to be in a certain place was connected to their relationships. Whilst many would want to be at home with the people they love, some are clear that they would prefer to be elsewhere if being at home would put their loved ones under excessive strain:

They might say, "Well I'd [rather] be at home, but really, it depends on how my family are, and if my family were really struggling then I would want it to be in the hospice." (Interview 1: Doctor)

Some professionals highlighted how this demonstrated that, whilst the person's choice was the primary consideration, the considerations of the people who are important to them also needed to be taken into account:

There has to be a bigger debate than what the patient wants, because if they choose home for instance, can the family cope with that? Is that too much for them or do they need medical intervention which is going to cause more difficulties for the family? (Interview 9: Chaplain)

Nonetheless, in those instances where a person could be at home with people who are important to them, this could make a big difference. We can see again how central a person's relationships are to their experience of dying. A number of the professionals we spoke to mentioned people's desire to have those important to them around at the end of life:

The things that people tend to want are - they usually want their family around, or loved ones around. (Interview 1: Doctor)

> *Where possible, to have a good death, they need to have the time and the space and the people that they want around them. (Interview 11: Nurse)*

Professionals again emphasised that the people who are important to someone may or may not include family:

> *For many...the families are the most important to them, they want to be surrounded by the family. Not always...people have different relationships don't they? (Interview 4: Chaplain)*

> *Some people want friends...quite often from a professional point of view you'll think that the family are the most important people to someone...until you actually talk to them, and find out from them who the important people are...often friends are more important than family. (Interview 10: Nurse)*

In some instances, those important to someone were not restricted simply to human beings:

> *A number of patients will ask to see pets if they can in their last few days of life. (Interview 10: Nurse)*

> *These quirky things that make the news...indicate what can be done and what can make a difference, such as the lady whose horse was brought to stick its neck through her window at the hospice, or people whose dogs come along, or that sort of thing. (Interview 2: Doctor)*

These findings demonstrate that a person's situated relationships are important to them as they approach the end of life. This includes their relationships with animals who are important to them as well as people. At the same time, it is important to be aware that this does not always mean that someone wants those people there at the very end of their lives.

There was a lady yesterday...very proud, very well-known in the village, lots of friends, very good social support – and what she said is, "When I reach the point where I'm unconscious, and I'm unable to talk to people and interact, I don't want people sitting round just gawping at me". (Interview 11: Nurse)

For the people who expressed such wishes, it was not usually a rejection of their relationships or their importance at the end of life. On the contrary:

Some people, they want people around them till the last minute, and they want someone holding their hand, and then other people they just say, "Look, I want my family to remember me...as best as possible". (Interview 11: Nurse)

Respect

A dignified death depends not just on having certain things or the presence of certain people – it also requires a certain kind of care. Compassion has been central to providing a number of the things we have seen that people ask for, from pain relief to seeing their pets. Compassionate care also requires that, in particular, a person's dignity is respected throughout. Professionals regarded the manner of care as essential for honouring the person's dignity:

[It's important to make] sure that they're covered up, and that they are respected, treated as a human being – to be treated as you would like to be treated. (Interview 6: Chaplain)

[It's important] to care for them, respecting their dignity... just making sure that we say right to the end, to the end of their earthly lives, "You matter". (Interview 7: Chaplain)

> *[Dignity is] about treating them with respect and making sure you can form a trusting relationship with them. (Interview 11: Nurse)*

For many of the professionals we spoke to, such respect was not just important when the person was aware of it. It applied, equally, to people who may not be conscious:

> *Continue to treat them with the same dignity if unconscious (or even dead) as you would someone who was conscious. (Interview 8: Doctor)*

Treating a seemingly unconscious person in this way is important partly because, as many professionals pointed out, one cannot be sure of how conscious a person is. Being unable to communicate does not necessarily mean that a person cannot understand at some level what is going on:

> *Even when you can say there's not much awareness there, I never know how true that is...I once had my appendix out. The muscle relaxant kicked in before the anaesthesia, so I'm literally on the operating table hearing everything...I heard [the surgeon] come in. And I thought, "I'd better say something" - and I couldn't open my mouth, couldn't open my eyes, move my limbs, because the muscle relaxant had kicked in, but the anaesthesia hadn't...So when somebody is close to death, seemingly divorced from what's going on around them, I'm not sure how much that thinking...is it like being asleep? Are you really aware of what's around you? (Interview 5: Doctor)*

> *We generally say...that hearing is the last sense to go, so...it's having that respect throughout all of your care. (Interview 10: Nurse)*

This is an especially important consideration when caring for people in the later stages of dementia, who may not be able to communicate but can still respond at least at an emotional level – they can feel a certain way even if they don't fully comprehend what is being said.[11] One doctor told us about a man in the later stages of advanced dementia who was distressed, aware that his wife was dying. The man was encouraged to stroke his wife's hand, which led to a positive change in his whole demeanour.

However, even if the person could not respond at an emotional level, it would be essential to remember that a person continues to be a person throughout the later stages of dementia and until their death. One study of the views of family carers of people with dementia reported that many participants emphasised that their relative was "still a person" with a life worth living: "The idea that he was not worth anything anymore made me very sad. He was still my dad."[12]

Similarly, it was important to continue to honour a person's dignity even if they were clearly unconscious. As one nurse put it:

> Although there's no communication with that person because they're imminently dying...you know that they were a person, and that they still are. (Interview 10: Nurse)

Professionals pointed out that this continues to be true after the person has died:

> [Respect] is equally [important] after the person has died... [it] is equally important that when the person is washed, maybe got ready for the relatives to see them, that that sort of respect is carried through. (Interview 7: Chaplain)

This is an argument also made by Michael Rosen in his *Dignity: Its History and Meaning*, referenced earlier in this essay. He argues that we should treat dead bodies with respect because we have a duty to perform acts that express our respect, irrespective of whether anyone is aware of or benefiting from these acts.[13] To truly respect the dignity that is intrinsic to humanity, we must observe this respect as a duty to all human beings, regardless of whether they are alive, unconscious, or no longer living.[14]

As noted above, central to meeting all of the end of life wishes discussed is a relationship between the professional and the person approaching the end of life, in which they are regarded as valuable. It was evident throughout our interviews with professionals that they showed people they were valued:

> *It might seem like an ordinary conversation when I'm asking them things about their lives, but actually what I'm doing is trying to find out and get them to remember who they are. You know, "You're not just this patient in this bed who've got this horrible disease. You've actually had a life and you've achieved wonderful things, you know - look at the children you've brought up, the grandchildren you've brought up." (Interview 4: Chaplain)*

> *I find that the most important thing is to listen to them and find out what their worries really are, without making assumptions. Because...it's sometimes too easy to make assumptions, but you've got to spend the time with them, listening to them, and finding out what their concerns really are. (Interview 6: Chaplain)*

Through this kind of respect for the person as they approach the end of life (and during and after their death), and an emphasis on meeting their needs and wishes, care professionals can help people to have a dignified death. In particular, they should aim to understand and meet (as far as possible) their needs and wishes in relation to enabling them to accept their death, doing what is necessary for them to develop peace of mind, relieving pain and other symptoms, enabling them to die in their place of choice where possible with the people who are important to them, meeting their spiritual or religious needs, and maintaining an attitude of respect for their personhood throughout.

Assisted dying

Given that a dignified death is experienced by many people, in the way we have outlined above, it may seem surprising that assisted dying is considered. Yet all of the care professionals told us that the topic had arisen with the people they care for – sometimes frequently:

> *There are people that want out of the whole dying process altogether, and request things like euthanasia that...obviously we can't provide. I get quite a lot of requests for that...I would say I get asked it at least once every two weeks. (Interview 1: Doctor)*

> *We'll get people who come in and say, "I wish I could just go to Switzerland" – or, "I wish you could just give me something just to finish me off". (Interview 7: Chaplain)*

Four main reasons why people made these requests arose from our interviews: feeling their suffering is unbearable; fearing humiliation from progressive illness and the dying process; fearing a loss of control; and not wanting to be a burden on services or people close to them. Professionals described the ways they responded to these fears and concerns. In all of their responses it was evident that their relationship with the person was essential to alleviating the concerns.

Suffering

As we would expect, feelings of unbearable suffering were prominent amongst those who spoke about assisted dying.

Some professionals spoke about people who responded to their own suffering – especially pain – by requesting assisted dying:

> *The occasional person does [mention assisted dying] – if they're in intractable pain, that, "Oh I wish you could give me something, but I know you can't." (Interview 6: Chaplain)*

However, in many cases, it was those close to the person, witnessing their suffering, who expressed their concerns. Analogies with suffering animals being put down were common – but professionals did not regard these comparisons as fair or accurate:

> *When people talk about assisted dying...the phrase that keeps coming up time and time again is, "Well you wouldn't treat an animal like this", "If there was a dog, they would be put down"... which is really sad, because I hate to hear them make those comparisons. (Interview 11: Nurse)*

> *If someone's dying over a long time, and the families are terribly worn out and distressed, they will say, you know, "Put an end to the suffering...you wouldn't let a dog die like this, it's terrible". (Interview 3: Doctor)*

> *And the phrase that they all say is, "You wouldn't treat an animal like this, you would put it down". But actually, it doesn't quite follow because we don't offer animals very good palliative care, do we? (Interview 1: Doctor)*

Can palliative care address these concerns? For many people, their suffering was relieved and symptoms managed by care professionals, which meant they no longer wanted assisted dying. What they had really wanted was not assisted dying, but relief from suffering:

And sometimes people are just mentioning it...they're not really seriously considering it, it's just, they're talking about it. Other people - they're thinking seriously about it. And quite often it's early on...and once the palliative care team have got involved and they've sorted pain relief and symptoms for them, things aren't always quite as stark. (Interview 4: Chaplain)

Sometimes people have said, "Well, I know you won't agree with it, but a few months ago I'd have seriously thought of going off to Switzerland"[15]...But then, if you can get it under control, then they feel very differently about it. (Interview 6: Chaplain)

I have certainly known people who have actually, their views have shifted. Sometimes people have this view because maybe they are in a lot of pain, or their symptoms are just so bad, they can't imagine them being improved. And sometimes with the right medication, with the right level of support, people can come to feel differently, and say, "I never imagined that my life could feel worth living again, but in fact now it does". (Interview 7: Chaplain)

These views were sometimes shaped by people perceiving their family member suffering terribly, when this was not a reflection of reality.

Often [the request for assisted dying] comes from relatives, and I think that is often an expression of their distress, because they'll say, 'Well you wouldn't treat an animal like this', but then you look at the patient and actually, they're in bed, they're completely comfortable, look really peaceful, asleep. And you think, well, the patient doesn't look like he or she is suffering - actually, they look very peaceful. But it's the distress of the relative that's going through that that is unbearable to them, so they just want that situation to go away. (Interview 1: Doctor)

71

In most cases where people want their suffering to end, therefore, it is possible for care professionals to relieve their suffering through the right medication. We also saw this earlier in this chapter when we looked at people's desire for pain-free death.

However, what happens in those few instances where this medication isn't enough, and people continue to be in unbearable pain? Professionals mentioned that in these occasional instances, it was legally and medically possible to increase their sedation. However, they also mentioned that once they had made clear that this option was possible, very few people actually asked for it:

I do sometimes...say, "I won't ever do anything that will kill you, but if you tell me this is intolerable, I'll ensure that you sleep." And if you give them that option, I very rarely have to actually increase someone's sedation. Sometimes they just want to feel calmer. (Interview 3: Doctor)

Some of the drugs that can make the person more comfortable may also have the side-effect of shortening a person's life:

If somebody is coming to the end of their lives, and they want to be less aware...a doctor will try to honour that – not in the sense of...giving them a drug which will kill them, but in terms of giving them a drug which will make them more comfortable, and may have the side-effect of actually meaning maybe that they don't live quite so long. (Interview 7: Chaplain)

It is important to note that this option is both legally and morally distinct from actively intervening with the intention of ending someone's life. This is based on the long-standing philosophical and theological concept of double effect famously articulated by Thomas Aquinas.[16] According to the doctrine of double effect, it is morally permissible to commit an act that causes harm as long as this is an unintended effect of the act, rather than the intention of it. Aquinas' example is killing an aggressor in self-defence – if the person defending themselves commits an act which causes the death of the aggressor, it is morally permissible as long as their intention was to save their own life.

Some may find this distinction between an act with intended effects and one with unintended (but foreseen) side-effects unconvincing. However, there are good reasons to regard this distinction as valid. As Nigel Biggar observes, if there were no distinction between these two, there would be no distinction between involuntary homicide and murder.[17] The distinction can be illustrated in the example of a mother who sees a wild animal approaching her child to attack them, and puts herself between them. She foresees that she will almost certainly die as a result of this, but her intention is to save her child's life, not to suffer a mauling.[18]

Therefore, we would argue that there is a morally significant distinction between administering symptom-relieving drugs to a person that may have the effect of shortening their life, and giving or assisting a person to take drugs that have the explicit purpose of ending their life.

In response to those who advocate assisted dying as a means to end a person's suffering, we would argue, in light of the evidence given to us by all the healthcare professionals we spoke to, that it is possible in most cases for medication to alleviate a person's suffering without any additional effects, and in those rare instances where this medication is insufficient, there is a morally and legally permissible option of administering drugs to make them more comfortable even if these drugs may shorten their lives.

Fear of humiliation

As noted above, in some cases people mention assisted dying not so much because they fear the suffering they will encounter, but the humiliation they may face as their body deteriorates and they approach the end of life. For some people, this is an explicit fear of losing their dignity:

> I think I hear the term [dignity] used most around physical care...like, "I need to have a nurse to wash my bum now, there's no dignity is there? I've lost my dignity." (Interview 1: Doctor)

This fear may be around humiliation from different aspects of illness or the care they need:

> People say that at the point where they need help with kind of toileting and things like that, "That's not me any more. I don't want to be like that – I don't want to be alive like that." (Interview 1: Doctor)

> For some people, it's not jumping in the bath in front of strangers with no clothes on that worries them, it's things like, "I don't want to be incontinent of faeces". (Interview 11: Nurse)

Just as it isn't difficult to understand why people fear unbearable suffering, it is easy to see why people would fear humiliation from nakedness or incontinence. In such cases, it becomes imperative that professionals caring for the person attempt to do what is necessary to alleviate their humiliation. With fears of nakedness and other aspects of care, it is essential that professionals treat the person with dignity. Canadian doctor Harvey Max Chochinov developed a 'Dignity in Care' framework for healthcare professionals, one aspect of which deals with privacy. One of its key "principles for care that enhances dignity" advises the professional to "safeguard the person's privacy: remember that procedures that may be routine for those who work in health care are not routine for most patients."[19] Chochinov also explains that there are other key ways to honour this dignity and enhance trust and connection between the professional and the person they are caring for:

> *Taking the time to ask patients their permission to perform an examination will make them feel less like a specimen to be poked and prodded and more like a person whose privacy is theirs to relinquish under mutually agreed conditions.*[20]

The professionals we spoke to told us that there are various options for dealing with symptoms such as incontinence:

> *Continence products now go from the range of small discreet pads that you can put inside your underwear, right through to full bowel regimes...in intensive care, your bowels can be managed for you, without any embarrassment or...cognition to yourself. (Interview 11: Nurse)*

They made clear that communicating with the person was essential, to understand what they most feared and what their priorities should be for addressing these fears.

> *I think the starting point...is communication, and getting the people to describe or communicate with you what it is that they need, and then, where possible you deliver that. So if someone says, "The last thing in the world I want is to be incontinent of faeces"...we can instigate regimes where we can use things like bowel irrigation...a medication regime, so that we can almost control when the bowel motions are likely to happen, and then*

manage the visitors...on the days where they're likely to happen.
(Interview 11: Nurse)

In many cases, then, the humiliation that people fear can be avoided by preventing the symptoms they fear will humiliate them. But what happens for those whose symptoms can't be prevented? Palliative care professionals are often experienced in caring for people under such circumstances:

[It's important that] when it's dealt with, it's done without any embarrassment to the individual, and it doesn't become a big issue for them or for anyone else. And all the care staff... devise strategies and their communication skills are such that people shouldn't feel degraded at all – they should just feel that it's part of their illness, and that it's managed as best as possible. (Interview 11: Nurse)

Sometimes other unavoidable symptoms can cause an unpleasant appearance or smell, which people may experience as humiliating. In such situations, how those around them respond to these symptoms is key, remembering and reflecting their inalienable relational worth as a human being:

This particular gentleman that I've been seeing recently, who's got this just horrible...facial tumour. He got the dressing off the other day, and it was so hard, because I'm a bit tickle-stomached about that kind of thing...But all the way through that conversation, I'm looking at his good side,...trying to show by my whole body language, by how I'm focused on him...that actually that's just a periphery...he's a valued human being. He is precious and he's important, and what he's saying to me is really important, and I feel that I need to portray that by how I am with him, as well as what is said. (Interview 4: Chaplain)

Once again, then, a major reason why people consider assisted dying can be addressed in the way in which people relate to them: by doing whatever they can to prevent symptoms which they find humiliating, and, where these are unavoidable, to respond in a way which shows the person that they are valued, thereby honouring their dignity.

Fear of losing control

In some instances, what people fear is not really the humiliation from symptoms themselves, but from their lack of control. This is something that people may be especially likely to fear with debilitating illnesses such as motor neurone disease (MND), which gradually cause the person to lose their communication and motor skills:

> I think sometimes [asking for assisted dying] is to do with that sense of lack of control - maybe somebody has always been very active and in charge of their lives, and the prospect of increasing weakness and debility is really, really hard. (Interview 7: Chaplain)

> Dignity in today's parlance means independence - I don't want to be dependent on somebody else, I don't want sickness to show...when people say, "This is undignified", sometimes they mean, "I'm not independent any more." (Interview 3: Doctor)

Professionals made clear that how the person is communicated with is fundamental in these situations. Building a relationship of trust with the person is crucial to helping alleviate their fears of losing control:

> They do sometimes plead for euthanasia because they're afraid of what's coming. There's something about relating to them in a way that, if you can get their trust, you can make the whole thing much better. (Interview 3: Doctor)

> *People can be helped to acknowledge that their circumstances have changed, and so their care needs...have changed...it's all part of ensuring that people recognise that their changing abilities, their increasing disabilities, are something that they can be helped to live with, and they can welcome the assistance that's offered and given. (Interview 2: Doctor)*

It was also important in such circumstances to recognise what the person could control, however limited, and ensure that they were given this opportunity. In some cases this can be around what seems like even trivial matters:

> *I think one of the important things...in the chaplain's role, is that people can actually just say to us, "Sorry, I really don't want to see you!" And that's in an area where very often people feel as if they have little control over their disease, I think that's a very important freedom to give people. (Interview 7: Chaplain)*

> *I think it's important for people, especially when...it feels that they've lost everything...to be able to have some control over whether they see you or not. So I think...it's really important for me to say, "Is it a good time or not? Do you want me to come?" or, "If you want me to go away, that's fine". They have control over very little else. (Interview 4: Chaplain)*

In addressing this fear it is once again important for professionals to consider the person's wishes and needs, and to meet these as far as possible:

> *We would always try to listen to what [the person's] priorities were and wishes were, and let them have choice as much as it's possible in what they want for the end of their life. (Interview 1: Doctor)*

This is especially important where a person fears loss of control. Respecting their wishes can help restore a feeling of some control, as well as enabling them to feel that they are valued – the source of their true dignity.

Fear of being a burden

For some of those who consider assisted dying, their fear is not around their own suffering, humiliation, or loss of control, but of the impact of their illness on others. They may fear being a burden on people who are important to them:

Sometimes people don't want to be a burden on their families – that's another [reason for mentioning assisted dying]. (Interview 7: Chaplain)

Some of the urge for assisted dying comes from compassion for family..."I don't want to be a burden" (Interview 3: Doctor)

Other people fear being a burden on a broader system, such as the NHS or the social care system:

You know, sometimes, you get people that won't even press the button [to call for help], because they feel they're just putting the nurses out or something. (Interview 9: Chaplain)

This is surely the most tragic reason why people request assisted dying, and goes against all we have said about people's dignity – their intrinsic worth because they are valued and loved, which demands that they are cared for in supportive relationships to the very end of their lives. Yet many worry that if assisted dying were legalised, this fear of being a burden would influence people's decision to end their own lives. One doctor said:

Assisted dying...has a financial benefit, not only to families but to government as well. You know...the pension crisis, the cost of healthcare, the challenges on the NHS...all the negative language around ageing. If we started to put assisted dying on the agenda,

you can probably expect some smart civil servant somewhere to
say, you know, "we've got the solution". (Interview 5: Doctor)

Again, other studies report people who fear "the idea of
a society not being able to afford all the people living as long
as they are. And some other country...saying, 'Look when you
reach 80, you have to have euthanasia'."[21]

This may seem like an extreme product of the imagination
to some, but such an idea has already been argued including
by one of Britain's leading moral philosophers, Baroness Mary
Warnock. Warnock argued that elderly people with dementia
should consider ending their own lives because they are a
burden on their families and the NHS – indeed, they may have
a "duty to die".[22] As dementia expert June Andrews says in
response to this:

I can think of nothing more tragic than where the person
wishes to kill himself or herself because of the burden they are to
other people. Other people have given them the view that they
are a burden.[23]

In particular, Andrews' last sentence on this is pertinent
– if a person feels that they are a burden, this is a view that
is influenced by others, as it is intrinsically related to their
connection with others. A person cannot consider himself
or herself a burden if there is no one on whom they are a
burden. With the ability to influence a person's perception of
themselves in this way, it is incumbent on those around them
to convey that, far from being a burden, they are valued. This
can be conveyed by the people who are important to them,
and must also be conveyed by professionals. The person should
be left in no doubt that they are worth spending time and
resources on to ensure that their needs and wishes are met as
far as possible.

Of course, there will be times when those they fear burdening, if they are a partner or family member for example, may legitimately feel that they are not able to care for the person. In such circumstances it is important to find a solution such as arranging homecare workers or for the person to be cared for in a care home or hospice. However, the message they communicate to the person at this time is of critical importance: to honour their dignity, they must convey the message that moving into a new care setting is to enable them to receive the high quality care they need and deserve, and to enable the person who had been their informal carer to continue their relationship with them. This is a very different message from the suggestion that the person is a burden from which their carer wishes to be relieved.

Evidence from the Netherlands, where euthanasia has been legal since 2001, also suggests that relationships can influence whether people consider this option. In a study by the Dutch National Institute for Health, it was found that loneliness or social isolation was a key factor in over half of the euthanasia requests reviewed.[24] Once again we see the fundamental importance of relationships for ensuring a person feels valued, and does not therefore consider the termination of their own life as preferable to living. Whether by alleviating the person's suffering, helping them to avoid humiliation or to deal with the loss of control that comes with progressive illness, or by enabling them to feel valued and worth investing in, professionals and those close to a person approaching the end of life can play a significant role in addressing their concerns and helping them to feel that assisted dying is not a preferable option over living and being cared for by people who value them.

---

[1] The range of experience in end of life care amongst these professionals was from two years to around thirty.

[2] We spoke to a minimum of two professionals in each of these roles, interviewing a total of eleven professionals. They are identified only by their role, to ensure anonymity.

[3] Ben Cosgrove, 'The Photo That Changed the Face of AIDS', *LIFE Magazine* (2015), *time.com/3503000/behind-the-picture-the-photo-that-changed-the-face-of-aids*, accessed 6 May 2017. The photo was taken by a journalism student named Therese Frare.

[4] Although 'family' was the term used in a number of these quotes, it is clear from these interviews that professionals would include in this anyone the person at the end of life considers important to them and wants to be part of the care process.

[5] Choice in End of Life Programme Board, *What's important to me: A Review of Choice in End of Life Care*, *www.gov.uk/government/publications/choice-in-end-of-life-care*, accessed 14 May 2017.

[6] Caroline Richmond, 'Dame Cicely Saunders', *BMJ* 331:7510 (2005), p. 238.

[7] Choice in End of Life Programme Board, *What's important*, p. 3.

[8] Leadership Alliance for the Care of Dying People, 'One Chance to Get it Right: Improving people's experience of care in the last few days and hours of life' (2014) *www.gov.uk/government/uploads/system/uploads/attachment_data/file/323188/One_chance_to_get_it_right.pdf*, accessed 14 May 2017.

[9] The Liverpool Care Pathway (LCP) was a generic approach to care for the dying developed from a model of care used in hospices. It faced substantial criticism and, after a review chaired by Baroness Julia Neuberger, was gradually phased out between July 2013 and July 2014. For more information see the report from the review, 'More Care, Less Pathway: A Review of the Liverpool Care Pathway' (2013), *www.gov.uk/government/publications/review-of-liverpool-care-pathway-for-dying-patients* accessed 14 May 2017.

[10] Attilio Stajano, *Only Love Remains: Lessons from the Dying on the Meaning of Life – Euthanasia or Palliative Care?* (W. Sussex: Clairview Books, 2015), p. 40.

[11] Alzheimer's Society, 'The later stages of dementia', Factsheet 417 (2012).

[12] E Tomlinson et al, 'Euthanasia and physician-assisted suicide in dementia: A qualitative study of the views of former dementia carers', in *Palliat Med. 2015* Sep; 29(8) p. 723.

[13] Rosen, *Dignity*, pp. 139-40.

[14] Rosen, *Dignity*, p. 160.

[15] A euphemism for assisted dying by attending the Dignitas clinic in Switzerland, which a number of professionals quoted.

[16] Aquinas, *Summa Theologica IIaIIae*, q. 64, a. 7, *newadvent.org/summa/3064. htm#article7*, accessed 21 May 2017.

[17] Nigel Biggar, *Aiming to Kill: The Ethics of Suicide and Euthanasia* (London: Darton, Longman and Todd, 2004), p. 67. Involuntary homicide does not, as Biggar later points out, absolve the person of ultimate responsibility for the person's death, but rather, is morally distinct from killing someone with the explicit intention of ending their life.

[18] Ibid, p. 80 (based on Germain Grisez, 'Toward a Consistent Natural-Law Ethics of Killing', in *The American Journal of Jurisprudence*, Volume 15, Issue 1 (1 January 1970) p. 90).

[19] HM Chochinov, 'Dignity in Care: Approach', *www.dignityincare.ca/en/ approach.html*, accessed 21 May 2017.

[20] HM Chochinov, 'Dignity and the essence of medicine: the A, B, C, and D of dignity conserving care', *BMJ* 334 (2007), p. 186.

[21] Tomlinson et al, *Euthanasia*, p. 724.

[22] Martin Beckford, 'Baroness Warnock: Dementia sufferers may have a "duty to die"', *The Telegraph*, 18 September 2008, *www.telegraph.co.uk/news/ uknews/2983652/Baroness-Warnock-Dementia-sufferers-may-have-a-duty-to-die.html*, accessed 21 May 2017.

[23] June Andrews, *Dementia: The One-Stop Guide: Practical advice for families, professionals, and people living with dementia and Alzheimer's Disease* (London: Profile Books, 2015), p. 97.

[24] Simon Caldwell, 'Most euthanasia deaths linked to loneliness, says Dutch study', *Catholic Herald* 18 February 2016, *www.catholicherald.co.uk/ news/2016/02/18/most-euthanasia-deaths-linked-to-loneliness-says-dutch-study*, accessed 21 May 2017.

Conclusion

We saw in the previous chapter how health and social care professionals build relationships with the people they care for as patients, to enable them to have a dignified death. According to the understanding of dignity presented in this essay, dignified dying is not simply based on autonomy, choice and control over the time and manner of one's death, but rather on one's ineradicable worth as someone who is loved and valued.

Respecting this fundamental relational worth, as our interviews with professionals showed, requires person-centred care that makes the person feel valued and loved. This is achieved by treating their needs and wishes as central, but also by honouring the relationships that are a fundamental part of their experience as a human being. This requires taking into account the needs and wishes of those who are important to them as well.

In order to achieve this, it is essential that all people at the end of life have access to high quality palliative care. There are a number of barriers to this – not least the lack of resources and adequate training for those professionals. Proper investment in both of these is essential for ensuring that people can receive care that enables them to have a death that honours their inalienable relational dignity as a human being.

Many proponents of assisted dying would argue that they also support the provision of high-quality palliative care, but that some people will still want assisted dying. However, we have also now seen that the four main concerns that lead people to consider assisted dying – suffering, fear of humiliation, fear of losing control and fear of being a burden – can largely be addressed in different ways through care professionals taking time and effort and building a relationship with the person. Suffering can be alleviated in most cases; a person can be spared humiliation through measures to help with symptoms such as incontinence, and through general sensitivity in the care provided for them; their feelings of losing control can be minimised by enabling them to take control over that which they can and making them feel valued and respected where they cannot; and they can be helped not to feel a burden by sending them the crucial message that they are valued and worth the time and investment of those supporting them, and the care system as a whole.

This last point is especially important in a time when we are influenced by the idea of economic efficiency and cost-benefit analysis, what Canadian philosopher Charles Taylor describes as "instrumental reason", the tendency to treat efficiency – "the best cost-output ratio" – as a measure of success.[1] In the context of assisted dying, this would involve weighing up the benefits of the person being cared for until they die naturally with the costs of providing their care, both to those involved in their care, and to an increasingly pressured health and social care system.

Some may find it implausible that such reasoning actually takes place when it comes to people's deaths, but we saw in the previous chapter that these kinds of concerns trouble people. Sometimes people worry about being a burden of their own accord, but others may be, directly or indirectly, given the message that they are a burden. One report published in 2013 found that 61% of people over 65 felt that society saw them as a burden and 57% thought that the media encouraged the idea that older people are a problem for society.[2] Other research confirms this. In a qualitative study of the views of older people on assisted dying, one participant said:

Where's the dividing line between the next step, where Big Brother comes along and says, "Well, okay...very few people over the age of X, let's call it 90, really make a valuable contribution to society; they take up space and they're a demand and even a drain on the health system; we keep on patching them up but they're going to die in a few years' time anyway and that's a waste of money, so let's knock 'em." Where's the dividing line?[3]

This is lamentable, but sadly should not come as a surprise. We saw in the previous chapter that influential philosopher Baroness Warnock made such an argument, and our societal discourse conveys this message in different ways and through different media. Furthermore, this message is conveyed about a number of other groups in society, including immigrants[4] and those who receive financial benefits from the state.[5]

The idea that people could be made to feel a burden by their families and friends may equally seem to be based on an unjustly pessimistic view of human nature. But unfortunately many people do feel this way. In many cases, it may be neither intentional nor malicious; but through subtle indications that the person is taking away from their family's normal life – meaning they can't go on holiday or need to cut down on their social life, for instance – they may start to receive this message.

By granting a person assisted dying in such circumstances, far from honouring their dignity, we would reinforce the message to them that they are not valued enough to be worth investing in, and therefore lack dignity.

Furthermore, legalising assisted dying and thereby enabling people to make this choice for this or other reasons could have further practical consequences. Having seen that our society increasingly sends the message that older people (and other groups) are burdens, it is not hard to imagine that a society in which assisted dying is granted for a few soon becomes a society in which more and more older people feel they ought to choose this option and relieve pressure on society and those important to them.

We have already seen that people fear being seen as or made to feel that they are a burden. To change the law in a way that potentially leads to an expansion in people choosing to end their own lives rather than be cared for at a cost to others would therefore risk an unequivocal violation of the principles of human dignity that we have espoused.

As a society we have an opportunity to send a clear message to those who are approaching the end of life. This involves all citizens, the media, health and care organisations, and politicians and decision-makers. Collectively we can work towards proper investment in end of life care that shows that those requiring this care, by virtue of being human beings (made in the image of God from a Christian perspective), have inalienable relational value and are therefore worthy of the time and resources required to provide their care. This kind of society is surely preferable to one in which the solution is people ending their own lives. The latter solution may be economically efficient and make people feel they have a choice; but it would ultimately reinforce a message that a person at the end of life is not unconditionally valuable. It would therefore fail truly to honour their dignity.

1 Charles Taylor, *The Ethics of Authenticity* (Cambridge, MA & London, England: Harvard University Press, 2003), p.5.

2 Royal Voluntary Service News, 'Major new report reveals flawed approach in traditional services for older people', *www.royalvoluntaryservice.org.uk/news-and-events/news/-major-new-report-reveals-flawed-approach-in-traditional-services-for-older-people*, accessed 10 June 2017.

3 Phillipa J Malpas et al, 'Why do older people oppose physician-assisted dying? A qualitative study' *Palliative Medicine* 28:4 (2014), p. 356.

4 See for example *MailOnline*, 'The true cost of our open borders revealed: EU migrants are MORE likely to have a job in the UK than British citizens', 7 June 2016, *www.dailymail.co.uk/news/article-3628840/The-true-cost-open-borders-revealed-EU-migrants-likely-job-UK-British-citizens.html*, accessed 10 June 2017.

5 See for example *MailOnline*, 'Britain's bill for disability benefits has soared from £2billion in today's money after WW2 to £37billion a year now', 26 December 2016, *www.dailymail.co.uk/news/article-4066706/Britain-s-bill-disability-benefits-soared-2billion-today-s-money-WW2-37billion-year-now.html*, accessed 10 June 2017.

Appendix: Interviews with professionals

The content of chapter 3, Dignity at the end of life, is based on eleven interviews with healthcare professionals. These interviews were conducted between January and March 2017, and were a combination of face-to-face and telephone interviews, with one interview conducted via email.

The professionals interviewed consisted of four chaplains, five doctors (three of whom are still practising in palliative care, whilst two have moved on to other roles but continue to be involved in palliative care), and two palliative care nurses. The professionals primarily had experience of caring in hospitals and hospices.

The interviews were based around a series of questions relating to:

— the professional's role and experience;

— their experiences when people they had cared for had a good death and when they did not;

— what people were most likely to ask for or consider important at the end of life;

— the professional's own understanding of dignity and how this affected the care they provided for people at the end of life and those important to them.